FAIRIES PUZZLE TIME

Let's Play Tag!

⭐ Game

🙂 Yes   ☹ No

🔁 Repeat

⬛ Stop

INTERNET CONNECTION REQUIRED FOR AUDIO DOWNLOAD.

To use this book with the Tag™ Reader you must download audio from the LeapFrog® Connect Application.
The LeapFrog Connect Application can be downloaded and installed at leapfrog.com/connect.

FAIRY
NAMES

DEW DROP
DANCE

FAIRY FIND

```
P U C R J Y W I N G K
G E K S T E M D P L
R O T C V D B G N E D B
F V Z A J Q V U J A Q A M
B E A K L U E C D F U F P
E Y M S F E A T H E R C S
X E Y G J L E P O L L E N
W Q T A I L J X S W K Y K
```

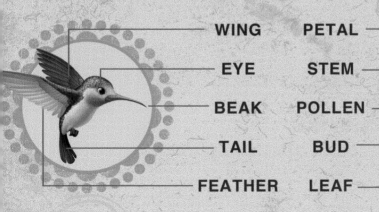

WING   PETAL

EYE   STEM

BEAK   POLLEN

TAIL   BUD

FEATHER   LEAF

The Perfect Rose

GARDEN GRAPH

	1	2	3	4	5
birch trees	🌳	🌳	🌳		
daisies	🌼				
lilies	🌸	🌸	🌸	🌸	🌸
maple trees	🌳	🌳			
tulips	🌷	🌷	🌷	🌷	

THAT THING!

⊛ RAINBOW TUNES

⊛ Rainbow Hues

Critter
Chorus

PIXIE HOLLOW

Spring

Summer

⊛ **Sounds**

⊛ **SEASON SENSE**

Sight

Smell

Autumn

Winter

of the Seasons

Touch

Hearing

Taste

Critter
Hide and
Seek

CRITTER TALK

PERFECT
PITCH!

angry
happy
sad
scared
surprised
thoughtful

Fairy Facts

FAWN

SILVERMIST

ROSETTA

IRIDESSA